CREATIVE TEACHING ASSOCIATES

Mr. Math

FAMOUS BLACK AMERICANS NUMBER PUZZLES

BOOK A

Graphics

STAN GERBRANDT
CAROL SCHMIDT

Cover Design

CAROL SCHMIDT

Larry Ecklund

This set of activities is designed to provide drill in addition and subtraction through a sequence of worksheets which includes basic addition and subtraction facts; two and three digit addition with and without regrouping; two and three digit subtraction, with and without regrouping; and column addition.

These worksheets are developmental in nature and provide very interesting information about "Famous Black Americans".

The students are to complete the problems, write the answers; then "code in" the letters for the answers in the spaces provided on each page. These letters "spell out" the names of the Famous Black Americans.

These arithmetic lessons can serve as a spring-board in your instructional program:

1. Do more research about each person.
2. Make special reports about history and each person.
3. Study the "times" of each person.
4. Study the "field" of each person.

PAGE	FAMOUS PERSON	MATH SKILL
1	ELLEN CRAFT	BASIC ADDITION FACTS
2	WILLIAM WELLS BROWN	BASIC ADDITION FACTS
3	ALEXANDER CRUMMELL	BASIC SUBTRACTION FACTS
4	JOE LOUIS	BASIC SUBTRACTION FACTS
5	ELMER SIMMS CAMPBELL	TWO—DIGIT ADDITION — NO REGROUPING
6	HENRY O. FLIPPER	TWO—DIGIT ADDITION — NO REGROUPING
7	MARY McLEOD BETHUNE	TWO—DIGIT ADDITION — REGROUPING
8	JAMES BECKWOURTH	TWO—DIGIT ADDITION — REGROUPING
9	GEORGE WASHINGTON CARVER	TWO—DIGIT ADDITION — REGROUPING
10	DR. DANIEL HALE WILLIAMS	TWO—DIGIT ADDITION — REGROUPING
11	DR. CHARLES DREW	ONE AND TWO—DIGIT SUBTRACTION — NO REGROUPING
12	JOHN HOPE FRANKLIN	TWO—DIGIT SUBTRACTION — NO REGROUPING
13	JESSE OWENS	TWO—DIGIT SUBTRACTION — REGROUPING
14	JOE GANS	TWO—DIGIT SUBTRACTION — REGROUPING
15	ALTHEA GIBSON	TWO AND THREE—DIGIT ADDITION — NO REGROUPING
16	JOSEPH CINQUE	TWO AND THREE—DIGIT ADDITION — NO REGROUPING
17	ISAAC MURPHY	TWO AND THREE—DIGIT ADDITION — REGROUPING
18	RALPH METCALFE	TWO AND THREE—DIGIT ADDITION — REGROUPING
19	WILLIE MAYS	TWO AND THREE—DIGIT ADDITION — REGROUPING
20	BENJAMIN O. DAVIS, JR.	TWO AND THREE—DIGIT SUBTRACTION — NO REGROUPING
21	GEN. FREDERIC E. DAVISON	TWO AND THREE—DIGIT SUBTRACTION — NO REGROUPING
22	MARY EDMONIA LEWIS	TWO AND THREE—DIGIT SUBTRACTION — REGROUPING
23	EDWARD M. BANNISTER	TWO AND THREE—DIGIT SUBTRACTION — REGROUPING
24	JOHN JAMES AUDUBON	TWO AND THREE—DIGIT SUBTRACTION — REGROUPING
25	WILT CHAMBERLAIN	ONE—DIGIT COLUMN ADDITION — 4 NUMERALS
26	LT. COL. MARGARET BAILEY	ONE—DIGIT COLUMN ADDITION — 5 NUMERALS
27	ARTHUR ASHE	TWO—DIGIT COLUMN ADDITION — 4 NUMERALS
28	FREDERICK DOUGLASS	TWO—DIGIT COLUMN ADDITION — 5 NUMERALS

Copyright © 1974
CREATIVE TEACHING ASSOCIATES
P. O. Box 7766, Fresno, California 93727
Printed in the United States of America

Famous Black Americans Puzzle

This woman escaped from slavery by pretending to be a white man. Her husband acted as her servant. They stayed in the finest hotels as they traveled to freedom in Philadelphia. This was one of the most daring escapes from slavery in American history without the help of the underground Railroads.

$$\overline{24}\ \overline{15}\ \overline{15}\ \overline{24}\ \overline{17}$$

$$\overline{20}\ \overline{9}\ \overline{14}\ \overline{19}\ \overline{11}$$

Complete the problems below. Use the code letters above each problem to find the name of this famous person.

A.	B.	C.	D.	E.
6 +8	1 +3	1 0 +1 0	8 +4	1 2 +1 2

F.	G.	H.	I.	J.
1 1 + 8	3 +5	9 +4	1 0 + 6	8 +2

K.	L.	M.	N.	O.
1 1 +1 1	8 +7	3 +4	9 +8	4 +1

P.	Q.	R.	S.	T.
0 +1	7 +5	6 +3	2 +0	6 +5

This man escaped from slavery and worked under Elijah Lovejoy against slavery. He was an anti-slavery lecturer and writer. In 1853 he became the first Afro-American to write and publish a novel, Clotelle. He also was an historian of the pre-Civil War period.

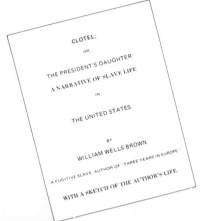

CLOTEL;
OR,
THE PRESIDENT'S DAUGHTER:
A NARRATIVE OF SLAVE LIFE
IN
THE UNITED STATES.

BY
WILLIAM WELLS BROWN

A FUGITIVE SLAVE; AUTHOR OF "THREE YEARS IN EUROPE."

WITH A SKETCH OF THE AUTHOR'S LIFE.

1	6	22	22	6	5	16

1	9	22	22	19

7	2	17	1	15

Complete the problems below. Use the code letters above each problem to find the name of this famous person.

A.	B.	C.	D.	E.	F.
3 +2	4 +3	5 +3	6 +6	6 +3	8 +5

G.	H.	I.	J.	K.	L.
7 +3	4 +0	2 +4	5 +6	8 +6	1 2 +1 0

M.	N.	O.	P.	Q.	R.
9 +7	8 +7	9 +8	1 0 +1 0	9 +9	2 +0

S.	T.	U.	V.	W.
1 0 + 9	1 1 +1 0	0 +0	1 2 +1 1	1 +0

Famous Black Americans Puzzle ③

Serving as an Episcopal minister in the United States, this man traveled to England and Africa. He was an anti-slavery speaker on three continents. He could not accept any idea that did not include black people as equals in the fellowship of man.

Africa

$$\overline{}_{1}\ \overline{}_{2}\ \overline{}_{4}\ \overline{}_{3}\ \overline{}_{1}\ \overline{}_{10}\ \overline{}_{8}\ \overline{}_{4}\ \overline{}_{7}$$

$$\overline{}_{6}\ \overline{}_{7}\ \overline{}_{5}\ \overline{}_{12}\ \overline{}_{12}\ \overline{}_{4}\ \overline{}_{2}\ \overline{}_{2}$$

Complete the problems below. Use the code letters above each problem to find the name of this famous person.

C.	N.	G.	S.	Q.
9 −3	2 0 −1 0	1 3 − 2	1 0 −1 0	2 2 −1 1

D.	T.	A.	M.	X.
9 −1	1 6 − 5	2 −1	1 2 − 0	6 −3

U.	B.	O.	F.	I.
6 −1	1 2 − 3	1 2 − 1	6 −6	2 −2

P.	R.	E.	L.	H.
1 0 − 1	1 4 − 7	5 −1	3 −1	1 4 − 5

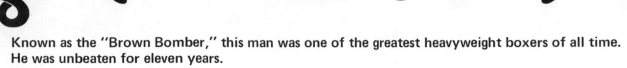

Famous Black Americans Puzzle 4

Known as the "Brown Bomber," this man was one of the greatest heavyweight boxers of all time. He was unbeaten for eleven years.

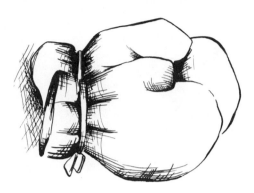

$$\overline{3} \quad \overline{9} \quad \overline{8}$$

$$\overline{12} \quad \overline{9} \quad \overline{11} \quad \overline{7} \quad \overline{0}$$

Complete the problems below. Use the code letters above each problem to find the name of this famous person.

A.
```
  1 6
- 1 2
```

B.
```
    6
-   5
```

C.
```
    8
-   6
```

D.
```
  1 0
-   6
```

E.
```
  1 2
-   4
```

F.
```
  1 0
-   4
```

G.
```
  1 3
-   3
```

H.
```
    9
-   7
```

I.
```
  1 5
-   8
```

J.
```
    9
-   6
```

K.
```
  1 3
-   7
```

L.
```
  1 4
-   2
```

M.
```
  1 5
-   5
```

N.
```
  1 5
-   9
```

O.
```
  1 0
-   1
```

P.
```
  1 4
- 1 2
```

R.
```
    6
-   4
```

S.
```
    8
-   8
```

T.
```
    8
-   4
```

U.
```
  1 6
-   5
```

Famous Black Americans Puzzle ⑤

This man won a national cartoon contest. He studied art at the Chicago Art Institute and later moved to St. Louis and then to New York. In New York he won national fame for his clever and humorous cartoons.

$$\overline{24}\ \ \overline{96}\ \ \overline{43}\ \ \overline{24}\ \ \overline{40}$$

$$\overline{70}\ \ \overline{75}\ \ \overline{43}\ \ \overline{43}\ \ \overline{70}$$

$$\overline{48}\ \ \overline{23}\ \ \overline{43}\ \ \overline{86}\ \ \overline{99}\ \ \overline{24}\ \ \overline{96}\ \ \overline{96}$$

Complete the problems below. Use the code letters above each problem to find the name of this famous person.

A.

  1 1
+1 2

B.

  8 5
+1 4

C.

  3 2
+1 6

E.

  1 2
+1 2

F.

  1 8
+3 1

H.

  1 2
+3 3

I.

  6 2
+1 3

K.

  6 3
+2 4

L.

  4 5
+5 1

M.

  3 1
+1 2

N.

  1 1
+1 8

P.

  7 5
+1 1

R.

  1 0
+3 0

S.

  2 0
+5 0

T.

  3 2
+5 2

U.

  2 5
+2 2

This man was the first Afro-American to be graduated from West Point. Following his graduation in 1877, he was assigned to the 10th Cavalry regiment in the southwest. He wrote a book called The Colored Cadet at West Point.

$$\overline{79} \ \overline{95} \ \overline{96} \ \overline{22} \ \overline{24} \ \ \ \ \overline{76} .$$

$$\overline{88} \ \overline{93} \ \overline{99} \ \overline{36} \ \overline{36} \ \overline{95} \ \overline{22}$$

Complete the problems below. Use the code letters above each problem to find the name of this famous person.

O.
```
  3 2
+ 4 4
─────
```

C.
```
  2 5
+ 1 2
─────
```

P.
```
  1 5
+ 2 1
─────
```

U.
```
  6 5
+ 1 0
─────
```

H.
```
  5 6
+ 2 3
─────
```

F.
```
  2 5
+ 6 3
─────
```

N.
```
  3 6
+ 6 0
─────
```

J.
```
  5 5
+ 2 2
─────
```

A.
```
  2 3
+ 3 2
─────
```

S.
```
  5 4
+ 1 1
─────
```

W.
```
  6 1
+ 1 2
─────
```

B.
```
  1 4
+ 1 2
─────
```

I.
```
  8 6
+ 1 3
─────
```

K.
```
  6 6
+ 3 2
─────
```

Q.
```
  4 4
+ 1 0
─────
```

R.
```
  1 0
+ 1 2
─────
```

E.
```
  8 3
+ 1 2
─────
```

L.
```
  1 1
+ 8 2
─────
```

Y.
```
  1 2
+ 1 2
─────
```

M.
```
  7 2
+ 2 5
─────
```

This woman devoted her life to bringing dignity, opportunity and hope to Black Americans. She became a teacher, a school builder, a public speaker and a worker in our government.

She started a school for girls in the Daytona Beach, Florida, area with only $1.50 in her pocket. She earned money for her school by doing many different jobs.

$$\overline{41} \ \overline{80} \ \overline{93} \ \overline{57}$$

$$\overline{41} \ \overline{51} \ \overline{94} \ \overline{60} \ \overline{72} \ \overline{44}$$

$$\overline{40} \ \overline{60} \ \overline{43} \ \overline{84} \ \overline{83} \ \overline{53} \ \overline{60}$$

Complete the problems below. Use the code letters above each problem to find the name of this famous person.

W.
```
  3 5
+3 5
```

C.
```
  1 9
+3 2
```

E.
```
  4 1
+1 9
```

N.
```
  2 9
+2 4
```

L.
```
  2 9
+6 5
```

A.
```
  4 4
+3 6
```

D.
```
  2 7
+1 7
```

O.
```
  4 8
+2 4
```

H.
```
  4 7
+3 7
```

T.
```
  2 7
+1 6
```

R.
```
  4 8
+4 5
```

Y.
```
  2 9
+2 8
```

B.
```
  2 5
+1 5
```

K.
```
  2 8
+1 7
```

U.
```
  4 6
+3 7
```

M.
```
  2 6
+1 5
```

This man was one of the most famous Indian fighters of his time. A friend of Kit Carson and Jim Bridger, he was a guide, Indian fighter, hunter, and the teller of tall tales. He discovered a pass across the Sierra Nevada Mountains which is named after him. It became one of the routes settlers used to get to the Northwest.

$\overline{34}\ \overline{30}\ \overline{31}\ \overline{90}\ \overline{32}$

$\overline{41}\ \overline{90}\ \overline{40}\ \overline{35}\ \overline{54}\ \overline{43}\ \overline{44}\ \overline{46}\ \overline{51}\ \overline{33}$

Complete the problems below. Use the code letters above each problem to find the name of this famous person.

E.	O.	A.	S.
$\begin{array}{r} 5\ 5 \\ +3\ 5 \\ \hline \end{array}$	$\begin{array}{r} 2\ 6 \\ +1\ 7 \\ \hline \end{array}$	$\begin{array}{r} 1\ 2 \\ +1\ 8 \\ \hline \end{array}$	$\begin{array}{r} 1\ 6 \\ +1\ 6 \\ \hline \end{array}$

K.	M.	C.	T.
$\begin{array}{r} 1\ 7 \\ +1\ 8 \\ \hline \end{array}$	$\begin{array}{r} 1\ 5 \\ +1\ 6 \\ \hline \end{array}$	$\begin{array}{r} 2\ 3 \\ +1\ 7 \\ \hline \end{array}$	$\begin{array}{r} 1\ 8 \\ +3\ 3 \\ \hline \end{array}$

H.	J.	U.	W.
$\begin{array}{r} 1\ 4 \\ +1\ 9 \\ \hline \end{array}$	$\begin{array}{r} 1\ 5 \\ +1\ 9 \\ \hline \end{array}$	$\begin{array}{r} 1\ 7 \\ +2\ 7 \\ \hline \end{array}$	$\begin{array}{r} 2\ 5 \\ +2\ 9 \\ \hline \end{array}$

B.	P.	R.	N.
$\begin{array}{r} 1\ 6 \\ +2\ 5 \\ \hline \end{array}$	$\begin{array}{r} 2\ 9 \\ +3\ 8 \\ \hline \end{array}$	$\begin{array}{r} 1\ 7 \\ +2\ 9 \\ \hline \end{array}$	$\begin{array}{r} 1\ 7 \\ +1\ 9 \\ \hline \end{array}$

Famous Black Americans
Puzzle ⑨

Known as the "Wizard of Tuskegee," this man developed over three hundred uses for the peanut. He was a friend of Henry Ford and helped scientists around the world. Because of his discoveries, new industries and new jobs were made for many workers.

$\overline{112}$ $\overline{118}$ $\overline{105}$ $\overline{113}$ $\overline{112}$ $\overline{118}$

$\overline{130}$ $\overline{102}$ $\overline{108}$ $\overline{122}$ $\overline{115}$ $\overline{123}$ $\overline{112}$ $\overline{117}$ $\overline{105}$ $\overline{123}$

$\overline{110}$ $\overline{102}$ $\overline{113}$ $\overline{101}$ $\overline{118}$ $\overline{113}$

Complete the problems below. Use the code letters above each problem to find the name of this famous person.

L.	C.	V.	H.
3 8 +6 9	3 6 +7 4	4 5 +5 6	4 8 +7 4

T.	M.	O.	I.
8 9 +2 8	4 6 +6 5	1 6 +8 9	8 8 +2 7

G.	A.	P.	S.
5 5 +5 7	1 3 +8 9	3 8 +8 8	4 9 +5 9

W.	E.	R.	N.
8 5 +4 5	7 9 +3 9	6 6 +4 7	3 9 +8 4

Famous Black Americans Puzzle ⑩

Medical history was made in the year 1893 by this famous doctor. A man with a knife wound close to his heart was near death. To save the patient's life, the doctor operated and sewed up the wound. The patient lived. It was the first successful heart operation on record.

$$\overline{173}\ \overline{120}\qquad \overline{173}\ \overline{131}\ \overline{147}\ \overline{158}\ \overline{160}\ \overline{174}$$

$$\overline{190}\ \overline{131}\ \overline{174}\ \overline{160}$$

$$\overline{198}\ \overline{158}\ \overline{174}\ \overline{174}\ \overline{158}\ \overline{131}\ \overline{137}\ \overline{112}$$

Complete the problems below. Use the code letters above each problem to find the name of this famous person.

V.
```
  7 8
+ 5 8
```

D.
```
  7 4
+ 9 9
```

L.
```
  8 7
+ 8 7
```

H.
```
  9 3
+ 9 7
```

A.
```
  6 9
+ 6 2
```

T.
```
  4 9
+ 8 9
```

J.
```
  6 5
+ 6 7
```

M.
```
  3 9
+ 9 8
```

N.
```
  6 8
+ 7 9
```

E.
```
  6 8
+ 9 2
```

W.
```
  9 9
+ 9 9
```

I.
```
  6 9
+ 8 9
```

P.
```
  6 9
+ 8 8
```

S.
```
  1 4
+ 9 8
```

Q.
```
  9 8
+ 9 4
```

R.
```
  6 1
+ 5 9
```

This man was a doctor and made one of the most important contributions to the Allied victory in World War II. He developed a way of changing blood into plasma. This important discovery has saved many thousands of lives each year since 1940.

$$\overline{13}\ \overline{50}$$

$$\overline{60}\ \overline{80}\ \overline{22}\ \overline{50}\ \overline{24}\ \overline{51}\ \overline{34}$$

$$\overline{13}\ \overline{50}\ \overline{51}\ \overline{15}$$

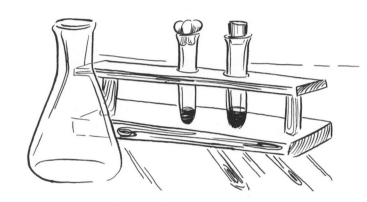

Complete the problems below. Use the code letters above each problem to find the name of this famous person.

D.	K.	F.	W.
1 9 − 6	2 5 −1 3	3 8 − 7	3 7 −2 2

L.	A.	E.	T.
3 8 −1 4	2 5 − 3	5 6 − 5	2 9 −1 8

B.	M.	S.	H.
4 6 − 4	5 6 −1 3	4 7 −1 3	8 4 − 4

J.	C.	O.	R.
9 4 − 4	6 3 − 3	6 2 −4 2	7 5 −2 5

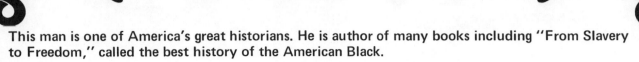

This man is one of America's great historians. He is author of many books including "From Slavery to Freedom," called the best history of the American Black.

$$\overline{44} \ \overline{11} \ \overline{63} \ \overline{38}$$

$$\overline{63} \ \overline{11} \ \overline{62} \ \overline{53}$$

$$\overline{33} \ \overline{10} \ \overline{31} \ \overline{38} \ \overline{27} \ \overline{14} \ \overline{20} \ \overline{38}$$

Complete the problems below. Use the code letters above each problem to find the name of this famous person.

T.	J.	O.	F.
5 2	6 6	9 4	9 4
−3 1	−2 2	−8 3	−6 1

D.	I.	K.	V.
2 7	7 1	8 9	4 8
−1 5	−5 1	−6 2	−3 2

P.	A.	R.	S.
7 4	3 9	8 7	7 6
−1 2	− 8	−7 7	−3 1

E.	N.	L.	H.
7 4	4 9	2 5	8 9
−2 1	−1 1	−1 1	−2 6

Famous Black Americans Puzzle

In the Berlin, Germany, Olympics of 1936 this athlete raced to victories in the 100 and 200 meter sprints. He also led the 400 meter relay team to its triumph and set an olympic running broad jump record. He won for himself the title of "Trackman of the Age."

$$\overline{23} \ \overline{16} \ \overline{24} \ \overline{24} \ \overline{16}$$

$$\overline{73} \ \overline{56} \ \overline{16} \ \overline{43} \ \overline{24}$$

Complete the problems below. Use the code letters above each problem to find the name of this famous person.

D.	R.	S.	J.
5 3 −3 4	3 0 −1 5	5 2 −2 8	4 1 −1 8

H.	V.	N.	P.
7 3 −2 5	9 1 −4 6	7 0 −2 7	9 2 −1 6

O.	U.	A.	E.
9 1 −1 8	3 1 −1 4	2 5 −1 6	3 2 −1 6

W.	I.	G.	F.
8 3 −2 7	3 6 −1 8	9 2 −4 8	8 4 −3 5

© 1974 Creative Teaching Associates

Famous Black Americans Puzzle ⑭

Many boxing authorities claim that this man was the greatest prize-fighter of all times. He was called the "Old Master" while still a young man. He fought — and defeated — fighters in higher weight divisions. The former lightweight champion's last fight took place in Baltimore; it was against tuberculosis, and he did not win.

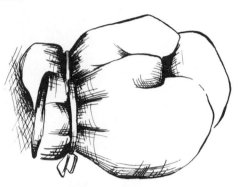

$$\overline{12} \quad \overline{74} \quad \overline{56}$$

$$\overline{76} \quad \overline{23} \quad \overline{53} \quad \overline{57}$$

Complete the problems below. Use the code letters above each problem to find the name of this famous person.

N.	C.	K.	T.
9 2	7 5	6 1	8 4
−3 9	−4 8	−3 6	−1 7

F.	S.	R.	G.
4 0	8 3	9 0	9 4
−2 6	−2 6	−4 5	−1 8

B.	J.	A.	O.
7 3	4 1	6 1	9 1
−2 7	−2 9	−3 8	−1 7

P.	E.	I.	U.
5 3	9 3	8 5	6 6
−2 5	−3 7	−1 9	−4 9

Until 1957 no black American of either sex had ever played in the finals of national tennis championships. In that year this woman won the United States Women's Singles title. It was her finest year. She won every important match. For the girl who started her career by playing paddle tennis in Harlem's streets, it was a dream come true.

$$\overline{155}\ \overline{479}\ \overline{698}\ \overline{688}\ \overline{366}\ \overline{155}$$

$$\overline{533}\ \overline{295}\ \overline{439}\ \overline{979}\ \overline{396}\ \overline{638}$$

Complete the problems below. Use the code letters above each problem to find the name of this famous person.

L.
```
  4 4 4
+   3 5
```

E.
```
  3 2 5
+   4 1
```

I.
```
  2 8 4
+   1 1
```

J.
```
  1 6 7
+   3 2
```

B.
```
  4 1 6
+   2 3
```

F.
```
  5 6 4
+   2 4
```

T.
```
  6 1 5
+   8 3
```

O.
```
  3 8 2
+   1 4
```

P.
```
  7 4 3
+   3 1
```

N.
```
  6 1 3
+   2 5
```

A.
```
  1 2 4
+   3 1
```

G.
```
  5 1 1
+   2 2
```

S.
```
  9 4 5
+   3 4
```

K.
```
  2 3 5
+   3 2
```

H.
```
  6 4 7
+   4 1
```

C.
```
  2 1 4
+   3 5
```

On board the ship "Amistad," an African slave, this man organized a revolt. He killed the captain, and tried to force the ship's owners to sail back to Africa. The ship's owners tricked this man and sailed north, where the ship was captured in 1839 off Long Island, New York. After a long trial, the Supreme Court said the men were to be free. Anti-slavery forces in the United States rejoiced.

177 648 773 199 481 888

699 588 238 395 949 199

Complete the problems below. Use the code letters above each problem to find the name of this famous person.

E.
```
  1 5 5
+   4 4
```

B.
```
  4 6 2
+   3 1
```

Q.
```
  3 3 0
+   6 5
```

L.
```
  5 6 2
+   2 2
```

C.
```
  6 6 6
+   3 3
```

A.
```
  3 4 1
+   5 2
```

J.
```
  1 4 4
+   3 3
```

T.
```
  8 1 5
+   6 0
```

S.
```
  7 5 3
+   2 0
```

H.
```
  8 3 3
+   5 5
```

O.
```
  6 0 5
+   4 3
```

G.
```
  6 3 3
+   4 4
```

P.
```
  4 3 0
+   5 1
```

N.
```
  2 0 4
+   3 4
```

I.
```
  5 6 6
+   2 2
```

U.
```
  9 0 9
+   4 0
```

Among the "little men" of sports this man's name looms big. Riding his first winning horse when he was only seventeen years of age, he went on to set a record unmatched in the history of racing. Before his career ended, he had scored 628 victories in 1,412 races. Kentucky was the birthplace of the nation's finest jockey.

<u>792</u> <u>393</u> <u>351</u> <u>351</u> <u>194</u>

<u>490</u> <u>984</u> <u>640</u> <u>766</u> <u>594</u> <u>495</u>

Complete the problems below. Use the code letters above each problem to find the name of this famous person.

H.
```
  5 5 5
+   3 9
```

M.
```
  4 5 8
+   3 2
```

C.
```
  1 5 8
+   3 6
```

V.
```
  7 3 7
+   1 9
```

E.
```
  8 3 9
+   4 3
```

A.
```
  3 2 5
+   2 6
```

P.
```
  7 4 7
+   1 9
```

R.
```
  6 0 6
+   3 4
```

N.
```
  3 4 8
+   1 7
```

S.
```
  3 7 7
+   1 6
```

Q.
```
  4 2 9
+   1 9
```

I.
```
  7 7 3
+   1 9
```

U.
```
  9 3 8
+   4 6
```

O.
```
  8 6 5
+   2 8
```

J.
```
  1 6 8
+   1 9
```

Y.
```
  4 0 9
+   8 6
```

Famous Black Americans
Puzzle 18

Born in Atlanta and raised in Chicago, this track star set college sprint records at Marquette University during the early 1930's. He ran in the 1932 and 1936 Olympics and was once co-holder of the world's record in the 100 yard dash.

$\overline{365}\ \overline{373}\ \overline{497}\ \overline{184}\ \overline{584}$

$\overline{687}\ \overline{753}\ \overline{460}\ \overline{481}\ \overline{373}\ \overline{497}\ \overline{867}\ \overline{753}$

Complete the problems below. Use the code letters above each problem to find the name of this famous person.

V.	K.	F.	H.
7 0 9 + 3 1	2 2 9 + 1 6	8 4 8 + 1 9	5 6 6 + 1 8

L.	P.	R.	T.
4 6 8 + 2 9	1 1 9 + 6 5	3 4 9 + 1 6	4 0 6 + 5 4

A.	S.	W.	C.
3 4 5 + 2 8	1 1 8 + 2 2	5 0 2 + 1 9	4 5 3 + 2 8

E.	M.	U.	O.
7 2 9 + 2 4	6 5 8 + 2 9	5 0 8 + 8 2	8 1 9 + 1 9

Famous Black Americans Puzzle 19

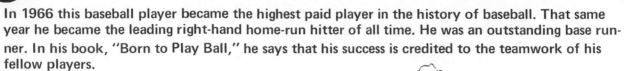

In 1966 this baseball player became the highest paid player in the history of baseball. That same year he became the leading right-hand home-run hitter of all time. He was an outstanding base runner. In his book, "Born to Play Ball," he says that his success is credited to the teamwork of his fellow players.

<u>   </u> <u>   </u> <u>   </u> <u>   </u> <u>   </u> <u>   </u>
564 220 550 550 220 800

<u>   </u> <u>   </u> <u>   </u> <u>   </u>
430 301 443 464

Complete the problems below. Use the code letters above each problem to find the name of this famous person.

G.
$$\begin{array}{r} 8\ 7\ 6 \\ +\ \ 2\ 4 \\ \hline \end{array}$$

L.
$$\begin{array}{r} 4\ 6\ 9 \\ +\ \ 8\ 1 \\ \hline \end{array}$$

W.
$$\begin{array}{r} 4\ 8\ 6 \\ +\ \ 7\ 8 \\ \hline \end{array}$$

D.
$$\begin{array}{r} 5\ 2\ 5 \\ +\ \ 7\ 5 \\ \hline \end{array}$$

E.
$$\begin{array}{r} 7\ 6\ 3 \\ +\ \ 3\ 7 \\ \hline \end{array}$$

J.
$$\begin{array}{r} 8\ 7\ 4 \\ +\ \ 6\ 6 \\ \hline \end{array}$$

R.
$$\begin{array}{r} 2\ 6\ 3 \\ +\ \ 4\ 9 \\ \hline \end{array}$$

U.
$$\begin{array}{r} 3\ 3\ 3 \\ +\ \ 8\ 9 \\ \hline \end{array}$$

A.
$$\begin{array}{r} 2\ 3\ 6 \\ +\ \ 6\ 5 \\ \hline \end{array}$$

H.
$$\begin{array}{r} 3\ 7\ 7 \\ +\ \ 2\ 3 \\ \hline \end{array}$$

M.
$$\begin{array}{r} 3\ 4\ 7 \\ +\ \ 8\ 3 \\ \hline \end{array}$$

S.
$$\begin{array}{r} 3\ 6\ 6 \\ +\ \ 9\ 8 \\ \hline \end{array}$$

C.
$$\begin{array}{r} 4\ 3\ 7 \\ +\ \ 6\ 3 \\ \hline \end{array}$$

I.
$$\begin{array}{r} 1\ 6\ 3 \\ +\ \ 5\ 7 \\ \hline \end{array}$$

Y.
$$\begin{array}{r} 3\ 8\ 8 \\ +\ \ 5\ 5 \\ \hline \end{array}$$

T.
$$\begin{array}{r} 8\ 2\ 9 \\ +\ \ 9\ 6 \\ \hline \end{array}$$

Famous Black Americans Puzzle ⟨20⟩

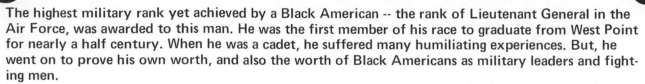

The highest military rank yet achieved by a Black American -- the rank of Lieutenant General in the Air Force, was awarded to this man. He was the first member of his race to graduate from West Point for nearly a half century. When he was a cadet, he suffered many humiliating experiences. But, he went on to prove his own worth, and also the worth of Black Americans as military leaders and fighting men.

His father had been the first Afro-American to have reached the rank of general in the United States Army.

$$\overline{223}\ \overline{311}\ \overline{314}\ \overline{334}\ \overline{323}\ \overline{611}\ \overline{124}\ \overline{314} \qquad \overline{731}.$$

$$\overline{621}\ \overline{323}\ \overline{134}\ \overline{124}\ \overline{643} \qquad \overline{334}\ \overline{156}.$$

Complete the problems below. Use the code letters above each problem to find the name of this famous person.

M.	E.	I.	J.
6 3 9 − 2 8	3 2 9 − 1 8	1 6 5 − 4 1	3 5 8 − 2 4

R.	B.	Y.	S.
1 9 9 − 4 3	2 4 6 − 2 3	5 8 9 − 6 6	6 5 6 − 1 3

D.	H.	V.	O.
6 3 2 − 1 1	9 7 6 − 4 2	1 4 6 − 1 2	7 7 9 − 4 8

N.	A.	W.	C.
3 4 5 − 3 1	3 6 5 − 4 2	3 9 2 − 4 1	5 6 4 − 3 4

He is the first black American general to have commanded American infantrymen in combat. He is third of his race in United States history to achieve the rank of general. The handsome former commander of the 199th Light Infantry Brigade was liked by his troops.

$\overline{613}\ \overline{133}\ \overline{740}\ \overline{133}\ \overline{103}\ \overline{232}\ \overline{402}$

$\overline{522}\ \overline{103}\ \overline{133}\ \overline{213}\ \overline{133}\ \overline{103}\ \overline{733}\ \overline{411}$

$\overline{133}\ .\qquad \overline{213}\ \overline{232}\ \overline{808}\ \overline{733}\ \overline{400}\ \overline{904}\ \overline{740}$

Complete the problems below. Use the code letters above each problem to find the name of this famous person.

F.	O.	I.	A.
5 6 3 − 4 1	9 1 6 − 1 2	7 6 5 − 3 2	2 7 5 − 4 3

D.	E.	K.	V.
2 9 4 − 8 1	1 6 6 − 3 3	3 1 5 − 1 5	8 8 8 − 8 0

J.	C.	G.	W.
2 6 9 − 1 3	4 8 8 − 7 7	6 8 9 − 7 6	2 6 5 − 4 1

L.	N.	S.	R.
4 6 3 − 6 1	7 6 5 − 2 5	4 7 5 − 7 5	1 6 6 − 6 3

She was the first black American to become famous in the field of sculpture. She received art training under Edmund Brackett in Boston. She moved to Rome, but returned periodically to exhibit her work in the United States. Among her finest works are portrait busts of prominent abolitionists John Brown and Charles Sumner.

$$\overline{478}\ \overline{189}\ \overline{676}\ \overline{157}$$

$$\overline{377}\ \overline{479}\ \overline{478}\ \overline{366}\ \overline{463}\ \overline{898}\ \overline{189}$$

$$\overline{88}\ \overline{377}\ \overline{459}\ \overline{898}\ \overline{838}$$

Complete the problems below. Use the code letters above each problem to find the name of this famous person.

D.
```
  5 3 6
-   5 7
```

J.
```
  2 5 3
-   6 5
```

N.
```
  5 6 1
-   9 8
```

S.
```
  9 1 4
-   7 6
```

B.
```
  3 4 2
-   5 3
```

E.
```
  4 2 5
-   4 8
```

I.
```
  9 4 3
-   4 5
```

W.
```
  5 3 1
-   7 2
```

M.
```
  5 2 4
-   4 6
```

P.
```
  8 3 1
-   4 7
```

R.
```
  7 6 5
-   8 9
```

A.
```
  2 3 5
-   4 6
```

O.
```
  4 6 4
-   9 8
```

F.
```
  8 9 3
-   9 4
```

L.
```
  1 8 1
-   9 3
```

Y.
```
  2 4 2
-   8 5
```

After winning a gold medal award at an exhibition in Philadelphia in 1876, this artist became increasingly appreciated. He painted landscapes and waterfront scenes and became the first black painter to win recognition by American art critics.

$$\overline{76}\ \ \overline{858}\ \ \overline{262}\ \ \overline{289}\ \ \overline{833}\ \ \overline{858}\ \ \ \ \ \ \overline{388}\ .$$

$$\overline{458}\ \ \overline{289}\ \ \overline{77}\ \ \overline{77}\ \ \overline{566}\ \ \overline{574}\ \ \overline{686}\ \ \overline{76}\ \ \overline{833}$$

Complete the problems below. Use the code letters above each problem to find the name of this famous person.

M.	L.	B.	S.
4 6 5 − 7 7	8 4 3 − 9 8	5 2 6 − 6 8	6 5 1 − 7 7

W.	A.	E.	P.
3 3 1 − 6 9	3 4 1 − 5 2	1 5 4 − 7 8	4 5 6 − 8 9

R.	T.	J.	D.
9 2 1 − 8 8	7 5 2 − 6 6	3 1 4 − 7 6	9 2 1 − 6 3

F.	U.	N.	I.
2 1 3 − 9 5	4 3 1 − 5 5	1 4 5 − 6 8	6 5 5 − 8 9

Famous Black Americans Puzzle ㉔

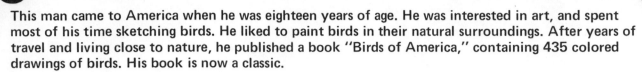

This man came to America when he was eighteen years of age. He was interested in art, and spent most of his time sketching birds. He liked to paint birds in their natural surroundings. After years of travel and living close to nature, he published a book "Birds of America," containing 435 colored drawings of birds. His book is now a classic.

$$\overline{692}\ \overline{230}\ \overline{384}\ \overline{69}$$

$$\overline{692}\ \overline{159}\ \overline{690}\ \overline{100}\ \overline{575}$$

$$\overline{159}\ \overline{889}\ \overline{429}\ \overline{889}\ \overline{99}\ \overline{230}\ \overline{69}$$

Complete the problems below. Use the code letters above each problem to find the name of this famous person.

U.	D.	H.	M.
9 2 5	5 0 6	4 8 0	7 6 2
− 3 6	− 7 7	− 9 6	− 7 2

B.	N.	G.	P.
1 3 6	1 4 8	3 9 5	4 1 9
− 3 7	− 7 9	− 9 7	− 9 9

S.	A.	E.	I.
6 5 1	2 0 5	1 3 6	6 5 3
− 7 6	− 4 6	− 3 6	− 5 8

J.	O.	C.	T.
7 9 1	3 0 8	3 0 0	7 4 3
− 9 9	− 7 8	− 4 5	− 7 5

This famous athlete is regarded by many experts as the greatest offensive player in basketball history. He is constantly double-teamed and roughed up, and yet has broken almost every scoring record in professional basketball.

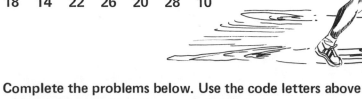

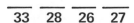

$\overline{\hspace{0.3cm}33\hspace{0.3cm}}$ $\overline{\hspace{0.3cm}28\hspace{0.3cm}}$ $\overline{\hspace{0.3cm}26\hspace{0.3cm}}$ $\overline{\hspace{0.3cm}27\hspace{0.3cm}}$

$\overline{\hspace{0.2cm}15\hspace{0.2cm}}$ $\overline{\hspace{0.2cm}13\hspace{0.2cm}}$ $\overline{\hspace{0.2cm}20\hspace{0.2cm}}$ $\overline{\hspace{0.2cm}34\hspace{0.2cm}}$ $\overline{\hspace{0.2cm}18\hspace{0.2cm}}$ $\overline{\hspace{0.2cm}14\hspace{0.2cm}}$ $\overline{\hspace{0.2cm}22\hspace{0.2cm}}$ $\overline{\hspace{0.2cm}26\hspace{0.2cm}}$ $\overline{\hspace{0.2cm}20\hspace{0.2cm}}$ $\overline{\hspace{0.2cm}28\hspace{0.2cm}}$ $\overline{\hspace{0.2cm}10\hspace{0.2cm}}$

Complete the problems below. Use the code letters above each problem to find the name of this famous person.

L.	B.	V.	M.	R.
7	3	8	9	6
6	4	9	8	6
5	5	6	8	5
+8	+6	+8	+9	+5

T.	A.	D.	J.	N.
6	2	5	4	2
5	4	9	4	2
7	6	6	4	3
+9	+8	+3	+4	+3

C.	W.	E.	I.	H.
2	9	2	9	3
1	8	4	5	2
4	8	2	5	5
+8	+8	+6	+9	+3

Famous Black Americans
Puzzle (26)

In 1944 this woman joined the Army Nurse Corps as a second lieutenant. While she was in the service she completed her education at San Francisco State College. On July 15, 1964, she became a Lieutenant Colonel. She has the highest rank of any black woman officer in the United States Army Nurse Corps and the first of her race to be so honored.

$\overline{23}$ $\overline{36}$. $\overline{19}$ $\overline{29}$ $\overline{23}$.

$\overline{22}$ $\overline{20}$ $\overline{18}$ $\overline{25}$ $\overline{20}$ $\overline{18}$ $\overline{14}$ $\overline{36}$

$\overline{15}$ $\overline{20}$ $\overline{27}$ $\overline{23}$ $\overline{14}$ $\overline{39}$

Complete the problems below. Use the code letters above each problem to find the name of this famous person.

C.	M.	U.	G.	B.
7	9	9	5	1
5	8	9	6	3
4	1	9	7	2
2	2	9	3	5
+1	+2	+9	+4	+4

I.	T.	W.	O.	L.
5	9	8	8	9
6	1	8	7	1
4	9	8	2	8
5	9	8	3	2
+7	+8	+8	+9	+3

A.	E.	N.	R.	Y.
2	5	9	8	9
4	3	1	2	8
3	1	2	4	9
6	2	1	2	8
+5	+3	+3	+2	+5

Famous Black Americans
Puzzle ㉗

At an age when most youngsters are just learning to use crayons, this man was learning to play tennis. By the time he was fifteen, he was playing — and winning — tournaments. He became the tennis team's outstanding player at U.C.L.A. He is the first of his race to be named to the United States Davis Cup team, and ranks with the world's great tennis stars.

$$\overline{60} \quad \overline{82} \quad \overline{93} \quad \overline{52} \quad \overline{61} \quad \overline{82}$$

$$\overline{60} \quad \overline{88} \quad \overline{52} \quad \overline{66}$$

Complete the problems below. Use the code letters above each problem to find the name of this famous person.

E.	T.	R.	B.	H.
1 3	3 9	2 3	1 9	1 3
2 4	1 9	2 9	1 1	1 6
1 6	1 8	1 1	1 7	1 1
+1 3	+1 7	+1 9	+1 5	+1 2

M.	C.	I.	L.	O.
1 5	3 5	2 1	2 2	1 6
1 3	2 5	3 6	1 4	1 3
2 1	1 8	1 5	1 2	1 3
+1 4	+1 2	+1 4	+1 1	+1 1

U.	A.	S.	G.	N.
1 3	1 3	3 1	1 4	1 3
1 7	1 7	2 1	1 6	1 2
1 9	1 8	1 2	1 3	1 5
+1 2	+1 2	+2 4	+1 1	+1 1

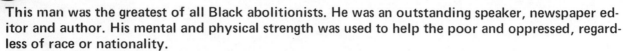

This man was the greatest of all Black abolitionists. He was an outstanding speaker, newspaper editor and author. His mental and physical strength was used to help the poor and oppressed, regardless of race or nationality.

He was a slave and was born in Maryland in 1817. He learned to read as a young boy, and spent most of his spare time improving this skill. When he was twenty-one years old, he escaped to the North.

$$\overline{348}\ \overline{129}\ \overline{217}\ \overline{132}\ \overline{217}\ \overline{129}\ \overline{142}\ \overline{199}\ \overline{293}$$

$$\overline{132}\ \overline{303}\ \overline{278}\ \overline{225}\ \overline{298}\ \overline{135}\ \overline{131}\ \overline{131}$$

Complete the problems below. Use the code letters above each problem to find the name of this famous person.

A.	F.	U.	O.	K.
2 5	5 3	4 7	8 7	1 4
3 6	6 2	4 8	9 8	7 5
1 4	8 1	5 7	6 5	8 6
2 8	9 4	5 8	3 2	9 5
+3 2	+5 8	+6 8	+2 1	+2 3

D.	I.	R.	B.	J.
1 0	2 3	1 7	3 5	2 5
1 1	1 2	1 8	2.8	3 6
3 4	4 5	2 9	4 9	4 2
5 6	2 6	2 8	3 1	3 5
+2 1	+3 6	+3 7	+4 2	+3 3

L.	C.	E.	S.	G.
4 5	2 2	2 2	2 7	1 3
6 5	4 6	5 6	2 9	5 2
3 2	3 7	3 3	2 5	4 6
9 8	4 3	8 1	2 6	8 9
+5 8	+5 1	+2 5	+2 4	+2 5

This woman escaped from slavery by pretending to be a white man. Her husband acted as her servant. They stayed in the finest hotels as they traveled to freedom in Philadelphia. This was one of the most daring escapes from slavery in American history without the help of the underground Railroads.

$$\underline{E}_{24} \quad \underline{L}_{15} \quad \underline{L}_{15} \quad \underline{E}_{24} \quad \underline{N}_{17}$$

$$\underline{C}_{20} \quad \underline{R}_{9} \quad \underline{A}_{14} \quad \underline{F}_{19} \quad \underline{T}_{11}$$

Complete the problems below. Use the code letters above each problem to find the name of this famous person.

A.
$$\begin{array}{r} 6 \\ +8 \\ \hline 14 \end{array}$$

B.
$$\begin{array}{r} 1 \\ +3 \\ \hline 4 \end{array}$$

C.
$$\begin{array}{r} 1\ 0 \\ +1\ 0 \\ \hline 20 \end{array}$$

D.
$$\begin{array}{r} 8 \\ +4 \\ \hline 12 \end{array}$$

E.
$$\begin{array}{r} 1\ 2 \\ +1\ 2 \\ \hline 24 \end{array}$$

F.
$$\begin{array}{r} 1\ 1 \\ +\ \ 8 \\ \hline 19 \end{array}$$

G.
$$\begin{array}{r} 3 \\ +5 \\ \hline 8 \end{array}$$

H.
$$\begin{array}{r} 9 \\ +4 \\ \hline 13 \end{array}$$

I.
$$\begin{array}{r} 1\ 0 \\ +\ \ 6 \\ \hline 16 \end{array}$$

J.
$$\begin{array}{r} 8 \\ +2 \\ \hline 10 \end{array}$$

K.
$$\begin{array}{r} 1\ 1 \\ +1\ 1 \\ \hline 2\ 2 \end{array}$$

L.
$$\begin{array}{r} 8 \\ +7 \\ \hline 15 \end{array}$$

M.
$$\begin{array}{r} 3 \\ +4 \\ \hline 7 \end{array}$$

N.
$$\begin{array}{r} 9 \\ +8 \\ \hline 17 \end{array}$$

O.
$$\begin{array}{r} 4 \\ +1 \\ \hline 5 \end{array}$$

P.
$$\begin{array}{r} 0 \\ +1 \\ \hline 1 \end{array}$$

Q.
$$\begin{array}{r} 7 \\ +5 \\ \hline 12 \end{array}$$

R.
$$\begin{array}{r} 6 \\ +3 \\ \hline 9 \end{array}$$

S.
$$\begin{array}{r} 2 \\ +0 \\ \hline 2 \end{array}$$

T.
$$\begin{array}{r} 6 \\ +5 \\ \hline 11 \end{array}$$

This man escaped from slavery and worked under Elijah Lovejoy against slavery. He was an anti-slavery lecturer and writer. In 1853 he became the first Afro-American to write and publish a novel, Clotelle. He also was an historian of the pre-Civil War period.

W I L L I A M
1 6 22 22 6 5 16

W E L L S
1 9 22 22 19

B R O W N
7 2 17 1 15

Complete the problems below. Use the code letters above each problem to find the name of this famous person.

A.	B.	C.	D.	E.	F.
3 +2 5	4 +3 7	5 +3 8	6 +6 12	6 +3 9	8 +5 13

G.	H.	I.	J.	K.	L.
7 +3 10	4 +0 4	2 +4 6	5 +6 11	8 +6 14	1 2 +1 0 2 2

M.	N.	O.	P.	Q.	R.
9 +7 16	8 +7 15	9 +8 17	1 0 +1 0 20	9 +9 18	2 +0 2

S.	T.	U.	V.	W.
1 0 + 9 19	1 1 +1 0 21	0 +0 0	1 2 +1 1 23	1 +0 1

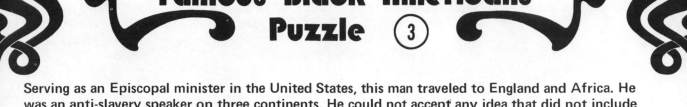

Serving as an Episcopal minister in the United States, this man traveled to England and Africa. He was an anti-slavery speaker on three continents. He could not accept any idea that did not include black people as equals in the fellowship of man.

A L E X A N D E R
1 2 4 3 1 10 8 4 7

C R U M M E L L
6 7 5 12 12 4 2 2

Africa

Complete the problems below. Use the code letters above each problem to find the name of this famous person.

C.	N.	G.	S.	Q.
9 −3 **6**	2 0 −1 0 **10**	1 3 − 2 **11**	1 0 −1 0 **0**	2 2 −1 1 **11**

D.	T.	A.	M.	X.
9 −1 **8**	1 6 − 5 **11**	2 −1 **1**	1 2 − 0 **12**	6 −3 **3**

U.	B.	O.	F.	I.
6 −1 **5**	1 2 − 3 **9**	1 2 − 1 **11**	6 −6 **0**	2 −2 **0**

P.	R.	E.	L.	H.
1 0 − 1 **9**	1 4 − 7 **7**	5 −1 **4**	3 −1 **2**	1 4 − 5 **9**

Known as the "Brown Bomber," this man was one of the greatest heavyweight boxers of all time. He was unbeaten for eleven years.

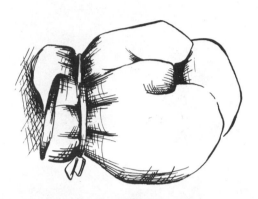

$$\frac{J}{3} \frac{O}{9} \frac{E}{8}$$

$$\frac{L}{12} \frac{O}{9} \frac{U}{11} \frac{I}{7} \frac{S}{0}$$

Complete the problems below. Use the code letters above each problem to find the name of this famous person.

A.
$$\begin{array}{r} 1\ 6 \\ -1\ 2 \\ \hline 4 \end{array}$$

B.
$$\begin{array}{r} 6 \\ -5 \\ \hline 1 \end{array}$$

C.
$$\begin{array}{r} 8 \\ -6 \\ \hline 2 \end{array}$$

D.
$$\begin{array}{r} 1\ 0 \\ -\ 6 \\ \hline 4 \end{array}$$

E.
$$\begin{array}{r} 1\ 2 \\ -\ 4 \\ \hline 8 \end{array}$$

F.
$$\begin{array}{r} 1\ 0 \\ -\ 4 \\ \hline 6 \end{array}$$

G.
$$\begin{array}{r} 1\ 3 \\ -\ 3 \\ \hline 10 \end{array}$$

H.
$$\begin{array}{r} 9 \\ -7 \\ \hline 2 \end{array}$$

I.
$$\begin{array}{r} 1\ 5 \\ -\ 8 \\ \hline 7 \end{array}$$

J.
$$\begin{array}{r} 9 \\ -6 \\ \hline 3 \end{array}$$

K.
$$\begin{array}{r} 1\ 3 \\ -\ 7 \\ \hline 6 \end{array}$$

L.
$$\begin{array}{r} 1\ 4 \\ -\ 2 \\ \hline 12 \end{array}$$

M.
$$\begin{array}{r} 1\ 5 \\ -\ 5 \\ \hline 10 \end{array}$$

N.
$$\begin{array}{r} 1\ 5 \\ -\ 9 \\ \hline 6 \end{array}$$

O.
$$\begin{array}{r} 1\ 0 \\ -\ 1 \\ \hline 9 \end{array}$$

P.
$$\begin{array}{r} 1\ 4 \\ -1\ 2 \\ \hline 2 \end{array}$$

R.
$$\begin{array}{r} 6 \\ -4 \\ \hline 2 \end{array}$$

S.
$$\begin{array}{r} 8 \\ -8 \\ \hline 0 \end{array}$$

T.
$$\begin{array}{r} 8 \\ -4 \\ \hline 4 \end{array}$$

U.
$$\begin{array}{r} 1\ 6 \\ -\ 5 \\ \hline 11 \end{array}$$

Famous Black Americans
Puzzle ⑤

This man won a national cartoon contest. He studied art at the Chicago Art Institute and later moved to St. Louis and then to New York. In New York he won national fame for his clever and humorous cartoons.

$\underset{24}{E}\ \underset{96}{L}\ \underset{43}{M}\ \underset{24}{E}\ \underset{40}{R}$

$\underset{70}{S}\ \underset{75}{I}\ \underset{43}{M}\ \underset{43}{M}\ \underset{70}{S}$

$\underset{48}{C}\ \underset{23}{A}\ \underset{43}{M}\ \underset{86}{P}\ \underset{99}{B}\ \underset{24}{E}\ \underset{96}{L}\ \underset{96}{L}$

Complete the problems below. Use the code letters above each problem to find the name of this famous person.

A.
```
  1 1
+1 2
-----
 2 3
```

B.
```
  8 5
+1 4
-----
 9 9
```

C.
```
  3 2
+1 6
-----
 4 8
```

E.
```
  1 2
+1 2
-----
 2 4
```

F.
```
  1 8
+3 1
-----
 4 9
```

H.
```
  1 2
+3 3
-----
 4 5
```

I.
```
  6 2
+1 3
-----
 7 5
```

K.
```
  6 3
+2 4
-----
 8 7
```

L.
```
  4 5
+5 1
-----
 9 6
```

M.
```
  3 1
+1 2
-----
 4 3
```

N.
```
  1 1
+1 8
-----
 2 9
```

P.
```
  7 5
+1 1
-----
 8 6
```

R.
```
  1 0
+3 0
-----
 4 0
```

S.
```
  2 0
+5 0
-----
 7 0
```

T.
```
  3 2
+5 2
-----
 8 4
```

U.
```
  2 5
+2 2
-----
 4 7
```

Famous Black Americans
Puzzle ⑥

This man was the first Afro-American to be graduated from West Point. Following his graduation in 1877, he was assigned to the 10th Cavalry regiment in the southwest. He wrote a book called The Colored Cadet at West Point.

$$\underset{79}{H} \quad \underset{95}{E} \quad \underset{96}{N} \quad \underset{22}{R} \quad \underset{24}{Y} \qquad \underset{76}{O}.$$

$$\underset{88}{F} \quad \underset{93}{L} \quad \underset{99}{I} \quad \underset{36}{P} \quad \underset{36}{P} \quad \underset{95}{E} \quad \underset{22}{R}$$

Complete the problems below. Use the code letters above each problem to find the name of this famous person.

O.	C.	P.	U.	H.
3 2 +4 4 **76**	2 5 +1 2 **37**	1 5 +2 1 **36**	6 5 +1 0 **75**	5 6 +2 3 **79**

F.	N.	J.	A.	S.
2 5 +6 3 **88**	3 6 +6 0 **96**	5 5 +2 2 **77**	2 3 +3 2 **55**	5 4 +1 1 **65**

W.	B.	I.	K.	Q.
6 1 +1 2 **73**	1 4 +1 2 **26**	8 6 +1 3 **99**	6 6 +3 2 **98**	4 4 +1 0 **54**

R.	E.	L.	Y.	M.
1 0 +1 2 **22**	8 3 +1 2 **95**	1 1 +8 2 **93**	1 2 +1 2 **24**	7 2 +2 5 **97**

Famous Black Americans Puzzle ⑦

This woman devoted her life to bringing dignity, opportunity and hope to Black Americans. She became a teacher, a school builder, a public speaker and a worker in our government.

She started a school for girls in the Daytona Beach, Florida, area with only $1.50 in her pocket. She earned money for her school by doing many different jobs.

M A R Y
41 80 93 57

M C L E O D
41 51 94 60 72 44

B E T H U N E
40 60 43 84 83 53 60

Complete the problems below. Use the code letters above each problem to find the name of this famous person.

W.
```
  3 5
+ 3 5
─────
  70
```

C.
```
  1 9
+ 3 2
─────
  51
```

E.
```
  4 1
+ 1 9
─────
  60
```

N.
```
  2 9
+ 2 4
─────
  53
```

L.
```
  2 9
+ 6 5
─────
  94
```

A.
```
  4 4
+ 3 6
─────
  80
```

D.
```
  2 7
+ 1 7
─────
  44
```

O.
```
  4 8
+ 2 4
─────
  72
```

H.
```
  4 7
+ 3 7
─────
  84
```

T.
```
  2 7
+ 1 6
─────
  43
```

R.
```
  4 8
+ 4 5
─────
  93
```

Y.
```
  2 9
+ 2 8
─────
  57
```

B.
```
  2 5
+ 1 5
─────
  40
```

K.
```
  2 8
+ 1 7
─────
  45
```

U.
```
  4 6
+ 3 7
─────
  83
```

M.
```
  2 6
+ 1 5
─────
  41
```

Famous Black Americans
Puzzle

This man was one of the most famous Indian fighters of his time. A friend of Kit Carson and Jim Bridger, he was a guide, Indian fighter, hunter, and the teller of tall tales. He discovered a pass across the Sierra Nevada Mountains which is named after him. It became one of the routes settlers used to get to the Northwest.

$$\underset{34}{J}\ \underset{30}{A}\ \underset{31}{M}\ \underset{90}{E}\ \underset{32}{S}$$

$$\underset{41}{B}\ \underset{90}{E}\ \underset{40}{C}\ \underset{35}{K}\ \underset{54}{W}\ \underset{43}{O}\ \underset{44}{U}\ \underset{46}{R}\ \underset{51}{T}\ \underset{33}{H}$$

Complete the problems below. Use the code letters above each problem to find the name of this famous person.

E.
```
  5 5
+ 3 5
-----
  90
```

O.
```
  2 6
+ 1 7
-----
  43
```

A.
```
  1 2
+ 1 8
-----
  30
```

S.
```
  1 6
+ 1 6
-----
  32
```

K.
```
  1 7
+ 1 8
-----
  35
```

M.
```
  1 5
+ 1 6
-----
  31
```

C.
```
  2 3
+ 1 7
-----
  40
```

T.
```
  1 8
+ 3 3
-----
  51
```

H.
```
  1 4
+ 1 9
-----
  33
```

J.
```
  1 5
+ 1 9
-----
  34
```

U.
```
  1 7
+ 2 7
-----
  44
```

W.
```
  2 5
+ 2 9
-----
  54
```

B.
```
  1 6
+ 2 5
-----
  41
```

P.
```
  2 9
+ 3 8
-----
  67
```

R.
```
  1 7
+ 2 9
-----
  46
```

N.
```
  1 7
+ 1 9
-----
  36
```

Famous Black Americans Puzzle ⑨

Known as the "Wizard of Tuskegee," this man developed over three hundred uses for the peanut. He was a friend of Henry Ford and helped scientists around the world. Because of his discoveries, new industries and new jobs were made for many workers.

G E O R G E
112 118 105 113 112 118

W A S H I N G T O N
130 102 108 122 115 123 112 117 105 123

C A R V E R
110 102 113 101 118 113

Complete the problems below. Use the code letters above each problem to find the name of this famous person.

L.
```
  3 8
+ 6 9
-----
  107
```

C.
```
  3 6
+ 7 4
-----
  110
```

V.
```
  4 5
+ 5 6
-----
  101
```

H.
```
  4 8
+ 7 4
-----
  122
```

T.
```
  8 9
+ 2 8
-----
  117
```

M.
```
  4 6
+ 6 5
-----
  111
```

O.
```
  1 6
+ 8 9
-----
  105
```

I.
```
  8 8
+ 2 7
-----
  115
```

G.
```
  5 5
+ 5 7
-----
  112
```

A.
```
  1 3
+ 8 9
-----
  102
```

P.
```
  3 8
+ 8 8
-----
  126
```

S.
```
  4 9
+ 5 9
-----
  108
```

W.
```
  8 5
+ 4 5
-----
  130
```

E.
```
  7 9
+ 3 9
-----
  118
```

R.
```
  6 6
+ 4 7
-----
  113
```

N.
```
  3 9
+ 8 4
-----
  123
```

Medical history was made in the year 1893 by this famous doctor. A man with a knife wound close to his heart was near death. To save the patient's life, the doctor operated and sewed up the wound. The patient lived. It was the first successful heart operation on record.

$$\underset{173 \quad 120}{\underline{D \quad R}} \qquad \underset{173 \ 131 \ 147 \ 158 \ 160 \ 174}{\underline{D \ A \ N \ I \ E \ L}}$$

$$\underset{190 \ 131 \ 174 \ 160}{\underline{H \ A \ L \ E}}$$

$$\underset{198 \ 158 \ 174 \ 174 \ 158 \ 131 \ 137 \ 112}{\underline{W \ I \ L \ L \ I \ A \ M \ S}}$$

Complete the problems below. Use the code letters above each problem to find the name of this famous person.

V.	D.	L.	H.
7 8 +5 8 136	7 4 +9 9 173	8 7 +8 7 174	9 3 +9 7 190

A.	T.	J.	M.
6 9 +6 2 131	4 9 +8 9 138	6 5 +6 7 132	3 9 +9 8 137

N.	E.	W.	I.
6 8 +7 9 147	6 8 +9 2 160	9 9 +9 9 198	6 9 +8 9 158

P.	S.	Q.	R.
6 9 +8 8 157	1 4 +9 8 112	9 8 +9 4 192	6 1 +5 9 120

Famous Black Americans Puzzle (11)

This man was a doctor and made one of the most important contributions to the Allied victory in World War II. He developed a way of changing blood into plasma. This important discovery has saved many thousands of lives each year since 1940.

<u>D</u> <u>R</u>
13   50

<u>C</u> <u>H</u> <u>A</u> <u>R</u> <u>L</u> <u>E</u> <u>S</u>
60   80   22   50   24   51   34

<u>D</u> <u>R</u> <u>E</u> <u>W</u>
13   50   51   15

Complete the problems below. Use the code letters above each problem to find the name of this famous person.

D.	K.	F.	W.
1 9 − 6 **13**	2 5 −1 3 **12**	3 8 − 7 **31**	3 7 −2 2 **15**

L.	A.	E.	T.
3 8 −1 4 **24**	2 5 − 3 **22**	5 6 − 5 **51**	2 9 −1 8 **11**

B.	M.	S.	H.
4 6 − 4 **42**	5 6 −1 3 **43**	4 7 −1 3 **34**	8 4 − 4 **80**

J.	C.	C.	R.
9 4 − 4 **90**	6 3 − 3 **60**	6 2 −4 2 **20**	7 5 −2 5 **50**

Famous Black Americans Puzzle

This man is one of America's great historians. He is author of many books including "From Slavery to Freedom," called the best history of the American Black.

$$\underset{44}{J}\ \underset{11}{O}\ \underset{63}{H}\ \underset{38}{N}$$

$$\underset{63}{H}\ \underset{11}{O}\ \underset{62}{P}\ \underset{53}{E}$$

$$\underset{33}{F}\ \underset{10}{R}\ \underset{31}{A}\ \underset{38}{N}\ \underset{27}{K}\ \underset{14}{L}\ \underset{20}{I}\ \underset{38}{N}$$

Complete the problems below. Use the code letters above each problem to find the name of this famous person.

T.
```
  5 2
 -3 1
 ----
   21
```

J.
```
  6 6
 -2 2
 ----
   44
```

O.
```
  9 4
 -8 3
 ----
   11
```

F.
```
  9 4
 -6 1
 ----
   33
```

D.
```
  2 7
 -1 5
 ----
   12
```

I.
```
  7 1
 -5 1
 ----
   20
```

K.
```
  8 9
 -6 2
 ----
   27
```

V.
```
  4 8
 -3 2
 ----
   16
```

P.
```
  7 4
 -1 2
 ----
   62
```

A.
```
  3 9
 -  8
 ----
   31
```

R.
```
  8 7
 -7 7
 ----
   10
```

S.
```
  7 6
 -3 1
 ----
   45
```

E.
```
  7 4
 -2 1
 ----
   53
```

N.
```
  4 9
 -1 1
 ----
   38
```

L.
```
  2 5
 -1 1
 ----
   14
```

H.
```
  8 9
 -2 6
 ----
   63
```

In the Berlin, Germany, Olympics of 1936 this athlete raced to victories in the 100 and 200 meter sprints. He also led the 400 meter relay team to its triumph and set an olympic running broad jump record. He won for himself the title of "Trackman of the Age."

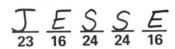

J E S S E
23 16 24 24 16

O W E N S
73 56 16 43 24

Complete the problems below. Use the code letters above each problem to find the name of this famous person.

D.	R.	S.	J.
5 3 −3 4 **19**	3 0 −1 5 **15**	5 2 −2 8 **24**	4 1 −1 8 **23**

H.	V.	N.	P.
7 3 −2 5 **48**	9 1 −4 6 **45**	7 0 −2 7 **43**	9 2 −1 6 **76**

O.	U.	A.	E.
9 1 −1 8 **73**	3 1 −1 4 **17**	2 5 −1 6 **9**	3 2 −1 6 **16**

W.	I.	G.	F.
8 3 −2 7 **56**	3 6 −1 8 **18**	9 2 −4 8 **44**	8 4 −3 5 **49**

Many boxing authorities claim that this man was the greatest prize-fighter of all times. He was called the "Old Master" while still a young man. He fought — and defeated — fighters in higher weight divisions. The former lightweight champion's last fight took place in Baltimore; it was against tuberculosis, and he did not win.

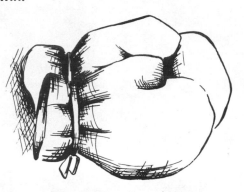

$$\frac{J}{12} \quad \frac{O}{74} \quad \frac{E}{56}$$

$$\frac{G}{76} \quad \frac{A}{23} \quad \frac{N}{53} \quad \frac{S}{57}$$

Complete the problems below. Use the code letters above each problem to find the name of this famous person.

N.	C.	K.	T.
9 2 −3 9 **53**	7 5 −4 8 **27**	6 1 −3 6 **25**	8 4 −1 7 **67**

F.	S.	R.	G.
4 0 −2 6 **14**	8 3 −2 6 **57**	9 0 −4 5 **45**	9 4 −1 8 **76**

B.	J.	A.	O.
7 3 −2 7 **46**	4 1 −2 9 **12**	6 1 −3 8 **23**	9 1 −1 7 **74**

P.	E.	I.	U.
5 3 −2 5 **28**	9 3 −3 7 **56**	8 5 −1 9 **66**	6 6 −4 9 **17**

Until 1957 no black American of either sex had ever played in the finals of national tennis championships. In that year this woman won the United States Women's Singles title. It was her finest year.
She won every important match. For the girl who started her career by playing paddle tennis in Harlem's streets, it was a dream come true.

A L T H E A
155 479 698 688 366 155

G I B S O N
533 295 439 979 396 638

Complete the problems below. Use the code letters above
each problem to find the name of this famous person.

L.
```
  4 4 4
+   3 5
-------
  4 7 9
```

E.
```
  3 2 5
+   4 1
-------
  3 6 6
```

I.
```
  2 8 4
+   1 1
-------
  2 9 5
```

J.
```
  1 6 7
+   3 2
-------
  1 9 9
```

B.
```
  4 1 6
+   2 3
-------
  4 3 9
```

F.
```
  5 6 4
+   2 4
-------
  5 8 8
```

T.
```
  6 1 5
+   8 3
-------
  6 9 8
```

O.
```
  3 8 2
+   1 4
-------
  3 9 6
```

P.
```
  7 4 3
+   3 1
-------
  7 7 4
```

N.
```
  6 1 3
+   2 5
-------
  6 3 8
```

A.
```
  1 2 4
+   3 1
-------
  1 5 5
```

G.
```
  5 1 1
+   2 2
-------
  5 3 3
```

S.
```
  9 4 5
+   3 4
-------
  9 7 9
```

K.
```
  2 3 5
+   3 2
-------
  2 6 7
```

H.
```
  6 4 7
+   4 1
-------
  6 8 8
```

C.
```
  2 1 4
+   3 5
-------
  2 4 9
```

On board the ship "Amistad," an African slave, this man organized a revolt. He killed the captain, and tried to force the ship's owners to sail back to Africa. The ship's owners tricked this man and sailed north, where the ship was captured in 1839 off Long Island, New York. After a long trial, the Supreme Court said the men were to be free. Anti-slavery forces in the United States rejoiced.

$$\underset{177}{J}\ \underset{648}{O}\ \underset{773}{S}\ \underset{199}{E}\ \underset{481}{P}\ \underset{888}{H}$$

$$\underset{699}{C}\ \underset{588}{I}\ \underset{238}{N}\ \underset{395}{Q}\ \underset{949}{U}\ \underset{199}{E}$$

Complete the problems below. Use the code letters above each problem to find the name of this famous person.

E.
```
  1 5 5
+   4 4
-------
  1 9 9
```

B.
```
  4 6 2
+   3 1
-------
  4 9 3
```

Q.
```
  3 3 0
+   6 5
-------
  3 9 5
```

L.
```
  5 6 2
+   2 2
-------
  5 8 4
```

C.
```
  6 6 6
+   3 3
-------
  6 9 9
```

A.
```
  3 4 1
+   5 2
-------
  3 9 3
```

J.
```
  1 4 4
+   3 3
-------
  1 7 7
```

T.
```
  8 1 5
+   6 0
-------
  8 7 5
```

S.
```
  7 5 3
+   2 0
-------
  7 7 3
```

H.
```
  8 3 3
+   5 5
-------
  8 8 8
```

O.
```
  6 0 5
+   4 3
-------
  6 4 8
```

G.
```
  6 3 3
+   4 4
-------
  6 7 7
```

P.
```
  4 3 0
+   5 1
-------
  4 8 1
```

N.
```
  2 0 4
+   3 4
-------
  2 3 8
```

I.
```
  5 6 6
+   2 2
-------
  5 8 8
```

U.
```
  9 0 9
+   4 0
-------
  9 4 9
```

Famous Black Americans Puzzle ⑰

Among the "little men" of sports this man's name looms big. Riding his first winning horse when he was only seventeen years of age, he went on to set a record unmatched in the history of racing. Before his career ended, he had scored 628 victories in 1,412 races. Kentucky was the birthplace of the nation's finest jockey.

$$\underset{792}{I}\ \underset{393}{S}\ \underset{351}{A}\ \underset{351}{A}\ \underset{194}{C}$$

$$\underset{490}{M}\ \underset{984}{U}\ \underset{640}{R}\ \underset{766}{P}\ \underset{594}{H}\ \underset{495}{Y}$$

Complete the problems below. Use the code letters above each problem to find the name of this famous person.

H.
```
  5 5 5
+   3 9
-------
  5 9 4
```

M.
```
  4 5 8
+   3 2
-------
  4 9 0
```

C.
```
  1 5 8
+   3 6
-------
  1 9 4
```

V.
```
  7 3 7
+   1 9
-------
  7 5 6
```

E.
```
  8 3 9
+   4 3
-------
  8 8 2
```

A.
```
  3 2 5
+   2 6
-------
  3 5 1
```

P.
```
  7 4 7
+   1 9
-------
  7 6 6
```

R.
```
  6 0 6
+   3 4
-------
  6 4 0
```

N.
```
  3 4 8
+   1 7
-------
  3 6 5
```

S.
```
  3 7 7
+   1 6
-------
  3 9 3
```

Q.
```
  4 2 9
+   1 9
-------
  4 4 8
```

I.
```
  7 7 3
+   1 9
-------
  7 9 2
```

U.
```
  9 3 8
+   4 6
-------
  9 8 4
```

O.
```
  8 6 5
+   2 8
-------
  8 9 3
```

J.
```
  1 6 8
+   1 9
-------
  1 8 7
```

Y.
```
  4 0 9
+   8 6
-------
  4 9 5
```

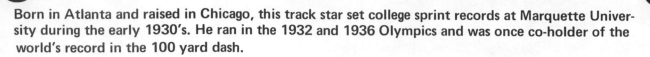

Born in Atlanta and raised in Chicago, this track star set college sprint records at Marquette University during the early 1930's. He ran in the 1932 and 1936 Olympics and was once co-holder of the world's record in the 100 yard dash.

R A L P H
365 373 497 184 584

M E T C A L F E
687 753 460 481 373 497 867 753

Complete the problems below. Use the code letters above each problem to find the name of this famous person.

V.	K.	F.	H.
7 0 9 + 3 1 740	2 2 9 + 1 6 245	8 4 8 + 1 9 867	5 6 6 + 1 8 584

L.	P.	R.	T.
4 6 8 + 2 9 497	1 1 9 + 6 5 184	3 4 9 + 1 6 365	4 0 6 + 5 4 460

A.	S.	W.	C.
3 4 5 + 2 8 373	1 1 8 + 2 2 140	5 0 2 + 1 9 521	4 5 3 + 2 8 481

E.	M.	U.	O.
7 2 9 + 2 4 753	6 5 8 + 2 9 687	5 0 8 + 8 2 590	8 1 9 + 1 9 838

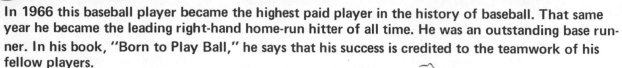

In 1966 this baseball player became the highest paid player in the history of baseball. That same year he became the leading right-hand home-run hitter of all time. He was an outstanding base runner. In his book, "Born to Play Ball," he says that his success is credited to the teamwork of his fellow players.

W I L L I E
564 220 550 550 220 800

M A Y S
430 301 443 464

Complete the problems below. Use the code letters above each problem to find the name of this famous person.

G.

```
  8 7 6
+   2 4
-------
  9 0 0
```

L.

```
  4 6 9
+   8 1
-------
  5 5 0
```

W.

```
  4 8 6
+   7 8
-------
  5 6 4
```

D.

```
  5 2 5
+   7 5
-------
  6 0 0
```

E.

```
  7 6 3
+   3 7
-------
  8 0 0
```

J.

```
  8 7 4
+   6 6
-------
  9 4 0
```

R.

```
  2 6 3
+   4 9
-------
  3 1 2
```

U.

```
  3 3 3
+   8 9
-------
  4 2 2
```

A.

```
  2 3 6
+   6 5
-------
  3 0 1
```

H.

```
  3 7 7
+   2 3
-------
  4 0 0
```

M.

```
  3 4 7
+   8 3
-------
  4 3 0
```

S.

```
  3 6 6
+   9 8
-------
  4 6 4
```

C.

```
  4 3 7
+   6 3
-------
  5 0 0
```

I.

```
  1 6 3
+   5 7
-------
  2 2 0
```

Y.

```
  3 8 8
+   5 5
-------
  4 4 3
```

T.

```
  8 2 9
+   9 6
-------
  9 2 5
```

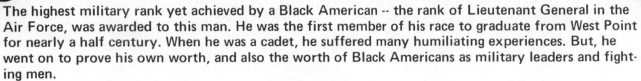

The highest military rank yet achieved by a Black American -- the rank of Lieutenant General in the Air Force, was awarded to this man. He was the first member of his race to graduate from West Point for nearly a half century. When he was a cadet, he suffered many humiliating experiences. But, he went on to prove his own worth, and also the worth of Black Americans as military leaders and fighting men.

His father had been the first Afro-American to have reached the rank of general in the United States Army.

$$\underset{223}{B}\ \underset{311}{E}\ \underset{314}{N}\ \underset{334}{J}\ \underset{323}{A}\ \underset{611}{M}\ \underset{124}{I}\ \underset{314}{N}\ \quad \underset{731}{O}.$$

$$\underset{621}{D}\ \underset{323}{A}\ \underset{134}{V}\ \underset{124}{I}\ \underset{643}{S}\ \quad \underset{334}{J}\ \underset{156}{R}.$$

Complete the problems below. Use the code letters above each problem to find the name of this famous person.

M.	E.	I.	J.
6 3 9 − 2 8 611	3 2 9 − 1 8 311	1 6 5 − 4 1 124	3 5 8 − 2 4 334

R.	B.	Y.	S.
1 9 9 − 4 3 156	2 4 6 − 2 3 223	5 8 9 − 6 6 523	6 5 6 − 1 3 643

D.	H.	V.	O.
6 3 2 − 1 1 621	9 7 6 − 4 2 934	1 4 6 − 1 2 134	7 7 9 − 4 8 731

N.	A.	W.	C.
3 4 5 − 3 1 314	3 6 5 − 4 2 323	3 9 2 − 4 1 351	5 6 4 − 3 4 530

He is the first black American general to have commanded American infantrymen in combat. He is third of his race in United States history to achieve the rank of general. The handsome former commander of the 199th Light Infantry Brigade was liked by his troops.

G E N E R A L
613 133 740 133 103 232 402

F R E D E R I C
522 103 133 213 133 103 733 411

E.   D A V I S O N
133   213 232 808 733 400 904 740

Complete the problems below. Use the code letters above each problem to find the name of this famous person.

F.
```
  5 6 3
-   4 1
─────
  5 2 2
```

O.
```
  9 1 6
-   1 2
─────
  9 0 4
```

I.
```
  7 6 5
-   3 2
─────
  7 3 3
```

A.
```
  2 7 5
-   4 3
─────
  2 3 2
```

D.
```
  2 9 4
-   8 1
─────
  2 1 3
```

E.
```
  1 6 6
-   3 3
─────
  1 3 3
```

K.
```
  3 1 5
-   1 5
─────
  3 0 0
```

V.
```
  8 8 8
-   8 0
─────
  8 0 8
```

J.
```
  2 6 9
-   1 3
─────
  2 5 6
```

C.
```
  4 8 8
-   7 7
─────
  4 1 1
```

G.
```
  6 8 9
-   7 6
─────
  6 1 3
```

W.
```
  2 6 5
-   4 1
─────
  2 2 4
```

L.
```
  4 6 3
-   6 1
─────
  4 0 2
```

N.
```
  7 6 5
-   2 5
─────
  7 4 0
```

S.
```
  4 7 5
-   7 5
─────
  4 0 0
```

R.
```
  1 6 6
-   6 3
─────
  1 0 3
```

She was the first black American to become famous in the field of sculpture. She received art training under Edmund Brackett in Boston. She moved to Rome, but returned periodically to exhibit her work in the United States. Among her finest works are portrait busts of prominent abolitionists John Brown and Charles Sumner.

$$\underline{M \quad A \quad R \quad Y}$$
478 189 676 157

$$\underline{E \quad D \quad M \quad O \quad N \quad I \quad A}$$
377 479 478 366 463 898 189

$$\underline{L \quad E \quad W \quad I \quad S}$$
88   377 459 898 838

Complete the problems below. Use the code letters above each problem to find the name of this famous person.

D.
$$\begin{array}{r} 536 \\ -\ 57 \\ \hline 479 \end{array}$$

J.
$$\begin{array}{r} 253 \\ -\ 65 \\ \hline 188 \end{array}$$

N.
$$\begin{array}{r} 561 \\ -\ 98 \\ \hline 463 \end{array}$$

S.
$$\begin{array}{r} 914 \\ -\ 76 \\ \hline 838 \end{array}$$

B.
$$\begin{array}{r} 342 \\ -\ 53 \\ \hline 289 \end{array}$$

E.
$$\begin{array}{r} 425 \\ -\ 48 \\ \hline 377 \end{array}$$

I.
$$\begin{array}{r} 943 \\ -\ 45 \\ \hline 898 \end{array}$$

W.
$$\begin{array}{r} 531 \\ -\ 72 \\ \hline 459 \end{array}$$

M.
$$\begin{array}{r} 524 \\ -\ 46 \\ \hline 478 \end{array}$$

P.
$$\begin{array}{r} 831 \\ -\ 47 \\ \hline 784 \end{array}$$

R.
$$\begin{array}{r} 765 \\ -\ 89 \\ \hline 676 \end{array}$$

A.
$$\begin{array}{r} 235 \\ -\ 46 \\ \hline 189 \end{array}$$

O.
$$\begin{array}{r} 464 \\ -\ 98 \\ \hline 366 \end{array}$$

F.
$$\begin{array}{r} 893 \\ -\ 94 \\ \hline 799 \end{array}$$

L.
$$\begin{array}{r} 181 \\ -\ 93 \\ \hline 88 \end{array}$$

Y.
$$\begin{array}{r} 242 \\ -\ 85 \\ \hline 157 \end{array}$$

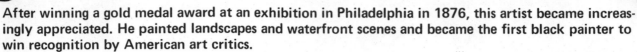

After winning a gold medal award at an exhibition in Philadelphia in 1876, this artist became increasingly appreciated. He painted landscapes and waterfront scenes and became the first black painter to win recognition by American art critics.

E D W A R D   M.
76 858 262 289 833 858   388

B A N N I S T E R
458 289 77 77 566 574 686 76 833

Complete the problems below. Use the code letters above each problem to find the name of this famous person.

M.	L.	B.	S.
4 6 5 − 7 7 **388**	8 4 3 − 9 8 **745**	5 2 6 − 6 8 **458**	6 5 1 − 7 7 **574**

W.	A.	E.	P.
3 3 1 − 6 9 **262**	3 4 1 − 5 2 **289**	1 5 4 − 7 8 **76**	4 5 6 − 8 9 **367**

R.	T.	J.	D.
9 2 1 − 8 8 **833**	7 5 2 − 6 6 **686**	3 1 4 − 7 6 **238**	9 2 1 − 6 3 **858**

F.	U.	N.	I.
2 1 3 − 9 5 **118**	4 3 1 − 5 5 **376**	1 4 5 − 6 8 **77**	6 5 5 − 8 9 **566**

Famous Black Americans Puzzle ㉔

This man came to America when he was eighteen years of age. He was interested in art, and spent most of his time sketching birds. He liked to paint birds in their natural surroundings. After years of travel and living close to nature, he published a book "Birds of America," containing 435 colored drawings of birds. His book is now a classic.

$$\underline{J\ O\ H\ N}$$
692 230 384 69

$$\underline{J\ A\ M\ E\ S}$$
692 159 690 100 575

$$\underline{A\ U\ D\ U\ B\ O\ N}$$
159 889 429 889 99 230 69

Complete the problems below. Use the code letters above each problem to find the name of this famous person.

U.
```
  9 2 5
-   3 6
-------
  8 8 9
```

D.
```
  5 0 6
-   7 7
-------
  4 2 9
```

H.
```
  4 8 0
-   9 6
-------
  3 8 4
```

M.
```
  7 6 2
-   7 2
-------
  6 9 0
```

B.
```
  1 3 6
-   3 7
-------
    9 9
```

N.
```
  1 4 8
-   7 9
-------
    6 9
```

G.
```
  3 9 5
-   9 7
-------
  2 9 8
```

P.
```
  4 1 9
-   9 9
-------
  3 2 0
```

S.
```
  6 5 1
-   7 6
-------
  5 7 5
```

A.
```
  2 0 5
-   4 6
-------
  1 5 9
```

E.
```
  1 3 6
-   3 6
-------
  1 0 0
```

I.
```
  6 5 3
-   5 8
-------
  5 9 5
```

J.
```
  7 9 1
-   9 9
-------
  6 9 2
```

O.
```
  3 0 8
-   7 8
-------
  2 3 0
```

C.
```
  3 0 0
-   4 5
-------
  2 5 5
```

T.
```
  7 4 3
-   7 5
-------
  6 6 8
```

This famous athlete is regarded by many experts as the greatest offensive player in basketball history. He is constantly double-teamed and roughed up, and yet has broken almost every scoring record in professional basketball.

W I L T
33 28 26 27

C H A M B E R L A I N
15 13 20 34 18 14 22 26 20 28 10

Complete the problems below. Use the code letters above each problem to find the name of this famous person.

L.	B.	V.	M.	R.
7	3	8	9	6
6	4	9	8	6
5	5	6	8	5
+8	+6	+8	+9	+5
26	18	31	34	22

T.	A.	D.	J.	N.
6	2	5	4	2
5	4	9	4	2
7	6	6	4	3
+9	+8	+3	+4	+3
27	20	23	16	10

C.	W.	E.	I.	H.
2	9	2	9	3
1	8	4	5	2
4	8	2	5	5
+8	+8	+6	+9	+3
15	33	14	28	13

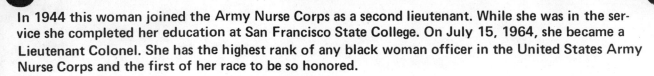

In 1944 this woman joined the Army Nurse Corps as a second lieutenant. While she was in the service she completed her education at San Francisco State College. On July 15, 1964, she became a Lieutenant Colonel. She has the highest rank of any black woman officer in the United States Army Nurse Corps and the first of her race to be so honored.

$$\underset{23}{L}\ \underset{36}{T}.\quad \underset{19}{C}\underset{29}{O}\underset{23}{L}.$$

$$\underset{22}{M}\underset{20}{A}\underset{18}{R}\underset{25}{G}\underset{20}{A}\underset{18}{R}\underset{14}{E}\underset{36}{T}$$

$$\underset{15}{B}\underset{20}{A}\underset{27}{I}\underset{23}{L}\underset{14}{E}\underset{39}{Y}$$

Complete the problems below. Use the code letters above each problem to find the name of this famous person.

C.	M.	U.	G.	B.
7	9	9	5	1
5	8	9	6	3
4	1	9	7	2
2	2	9	3	5
+1	+2	+9	+4	+4
18	22	45	25	15

I.	T.	W.	O.	L.
5	9	8	8	9
6	1	8	7	1
4	9	8	2	8
5	9	8	3	2
+7	+8	+8	+9	+3
27	36	40	29	23

A.	E.	N.	R.	Y.
2	5	9	8	9
4	3	1	2	8
3	1	2	4	9
6	2	1	2	8
+5	+3	+3	+2	+5
20	14	16	18	39

At an age when most youngsters are just learning to use crayons, this man was learning to play tennis. By the time he was fifteen, he was playing — and winning — tournaments. He became the tennis team's outstanding player at U.C.L.A. He is the first of his race to be named to the United States Davis Cup team, and ranks with the world's great tennis stars.

$$\underset{60}{A} \ \underset{82}{R} \ \underset{93}{T} \ \underset{52}{H} \ \underset{61}{U} \ \underset{82}{R}$$

$$\underset{60}{A} \ \underset{88}{S} \ \underset{52}{H} \ \underset{66}{E}$$

Complete the problems below. Use the code letters above each problem to find the name of this famous person.

E.
```
  1 3
  2 4
  1 6
+ 1 3
─────
  6 6
```

T.
```
  3 9
  1 9
  1 8
+ 1 7
─────
  9 3
```

R.
```
  2 3
  2 9
  1 1
+ 1 9
─────
  8 2
```

B.
```
  1 9
  1 1
  1 7
+ 1 5
─────
  6 2
```

H.
```
  1 3
  1 6
  1 1
+ 1 2
─────
  5 2
```

M.
```
  1 5
  1 3
  2 1
+ 1 4
─────
  6 3
```

C.
```
  3 5
  2 5
  1 8
+ 1 2
─────
  9 0
```

I.
```
  2 1
  3 6
  1 5
+ 1 4
─────
  8 6
```

L.
```
  2 2
  1 4
  1 2
+ 1 1
─────
  5 9
```

O.
```
  1 6
  1 3
  1 3
+ 1 1
─────
  5 3
```

U.
```
  1 3
  1 7
  1 9
+ 1 2
─────
  6 1
```

A.
```
  1 3
  1 7
  1 8
+ 1 2
─────
  6 0
```

S.
```
  3 1
  2 1
  1 2
+ 2 4
─────
  8 8
```

G.
```
  1 4
  1 6
  1 3
+ 1 1
─────
  5 4
```

N.
```
  1 3
  1 2
  1 5
+ 1 1
─────
  5 1
```

Famous Black Americans Puzzle

This man was the greatest of all Black abolitionists. He was an outstanding speaker, newspaper editor and author. His mental and physical strength was used to help the poor and oppressed, regardless of race or nationality.

He was a slave and was born in Maryland in 1817. He learned to read as a young boy, and spent most of his spare time improving this skill. When he was twenty-one years old, he escaped to the North.

F R E D E R I C K
348 129 217 132 217 129 142 199 293

D O U G L A S S
132 303 278 225 298 135 131 131

Complete the problems below. Use the code letters above each problem to find the name of this famous person.

A.	F.	U.	O.	K.
2 5	5 3	4 7	8 7	1 4
3 6	6 2	4 8	9 8	7 5
1 4	8 1	5 7	6 5	8 6
2 8	9 4	5 8	3 2	9 5
+3 2	+5 8	+6 8	+2 1	+2 3
135	348	278	303	293

D.	I.	R.	B.	J.
1 0	2 3	1 7	3 5	2 5
1 1	1 2	1 8	2 8	3 6
3 4	4 5	2 9	4 9	4 2
5 6	2 6	2 8	3 1	3 5
+2 1	+3 6	+3 7	+4 2	+3 3
132	142	129	185	171

L.	C.	E.	S.	G.
4 5	2 2	2 2	2 7	1 3
6 5	4 6	5 6	2 9	5 2
3 2	3 7	3 3	2 5	4 6
9 8	4 3	8 1	2 6	8 9
+5 8	+5 1	+2 5	+2 4	+2 5
298	199	217	131	225